HAPPINESS IS A WARM PUPPY

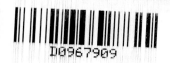

HAPPINESS IS A WARM PUPPY

BY CHARLES M. SCHULZ

SCHOLASTIC INC.
New York Toronto London Auckland
Sydney Mexico City New Delhi Hong Kong

ISBN 978-0-545-40023-7

Copyright 2006, PEANUTS © United Feature Syndicate, Inc.
All rights reserved. Published by Scholastic Inc., 557 Broadway,
New York, NY 10012, by arrangement with Cider Mill Press
Book Publishers. SCHOLASTIC and associated logos are
trademarks and/or registered trademarks of Scholastic Inc.

12 11 10 9 8 7 6 5 4 3 2 1 11 12 13 14 15 16/0

Printed in the U.S.A. 08

First Scholastic printing, September 2011

Design by: Jason Zamajtuk

HAPPINESS
IS A
WARM PUPPY

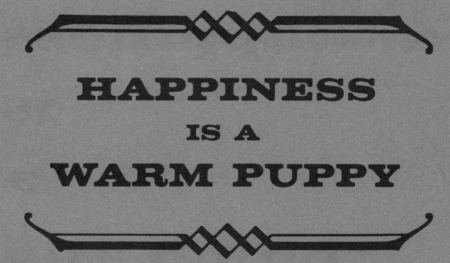

Happiness
is
a
thumb and
a blanket.

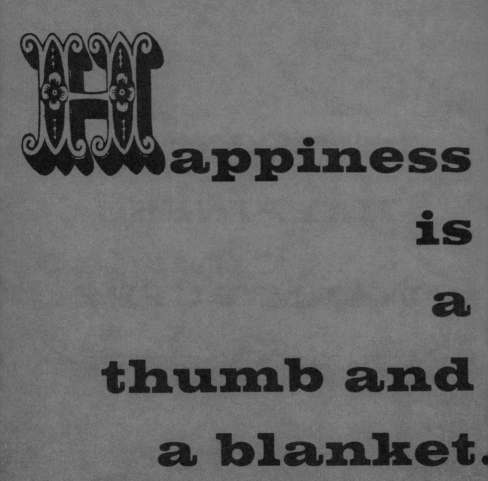

Happiness
is
an
umbrella
and a
new raincoat.

Happiness

is

a

pile

of leaves.

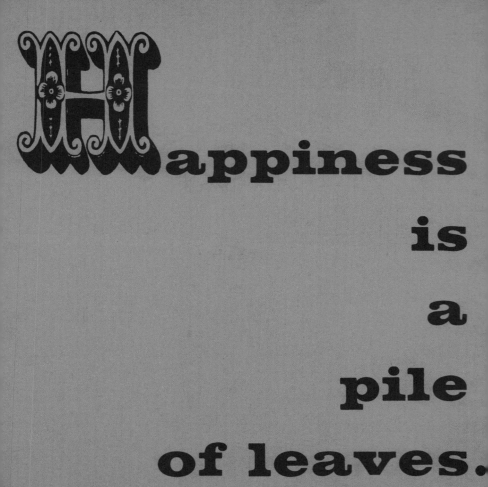

Happiness

is

a

warm

puppy.

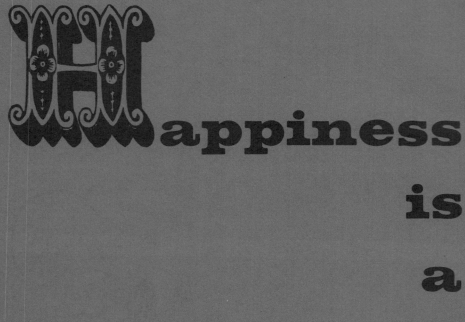

Happiness
is
an
"A"
on your
spelling test.

Happiness is finding someone you like at the front door.

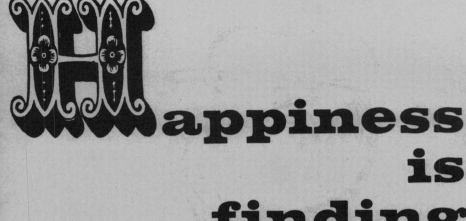

Happiness is three friends in a sandbox ...with no fighting.

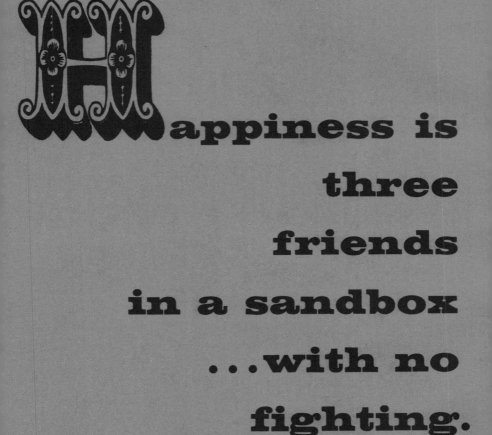

Happiness is sleeping in your own bed.

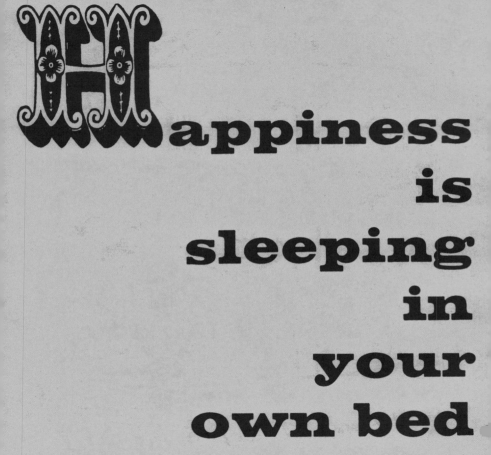

Happiness is a chain of paper clips.

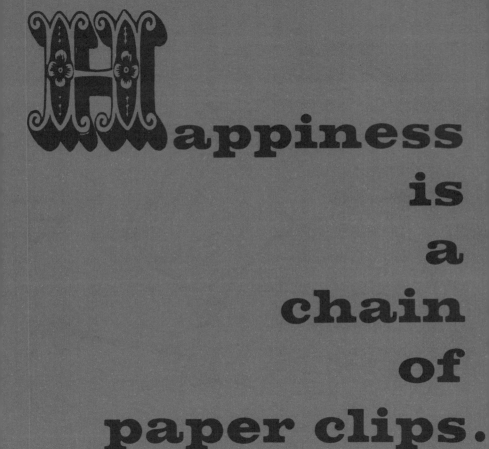

Happiness
is
getting
together
with
your friends.

Happiness
is
a
smooth
sidewalk

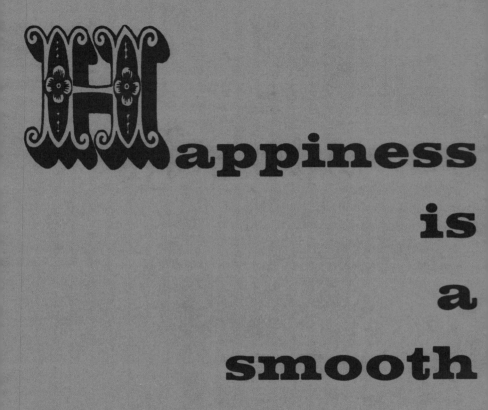

Happiness
is
finally
getting
the sliver
out

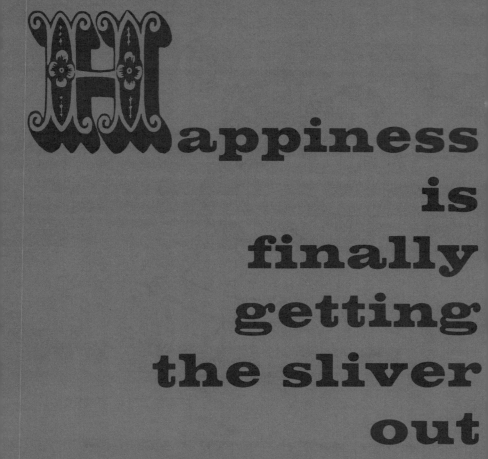

Happiness is a climbing tree

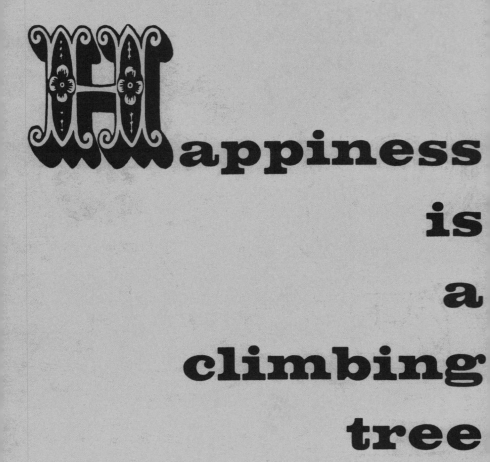

Happiness

is

lots

of

candles.

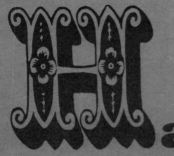

Happiness is being able to reach the doorknob

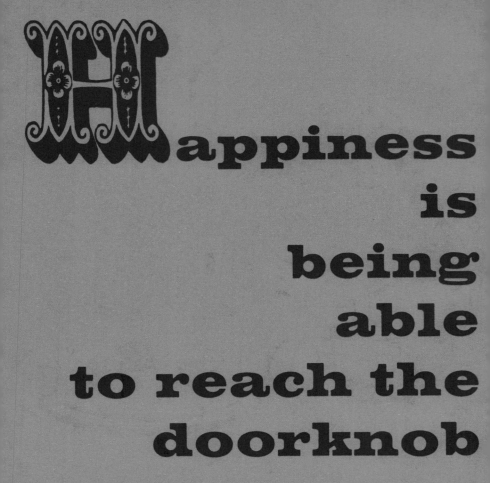

Happiness

is

knowing

all

the answers.

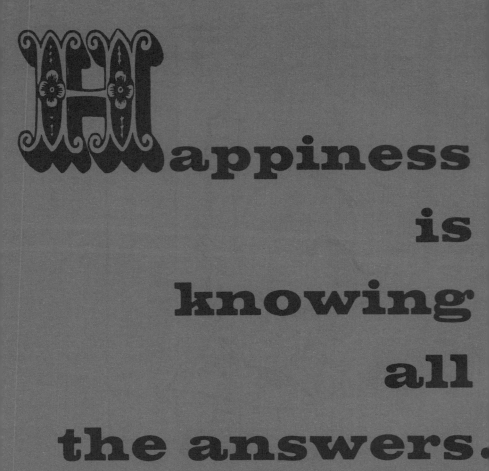

Happiness is a night light

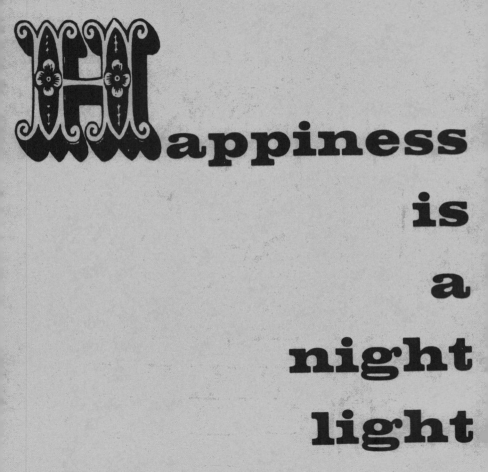

Happiness is some black, orange, yellow, white and pink jelly beans, but no green ones.

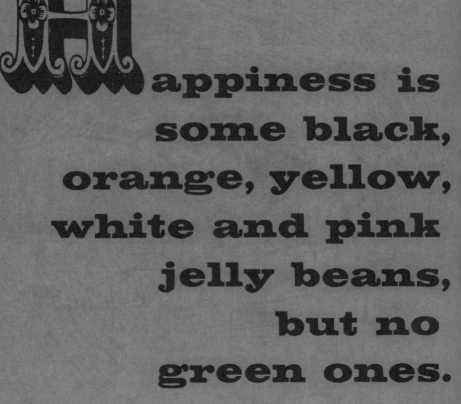

Happiness
is
the hiccups
...after
they've
gone away

Happiness
is
a
good
old fashioned
game of
hide and seek.

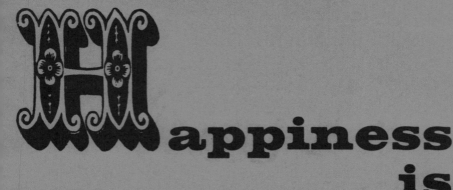

Happiness is a fuzzy sweater.

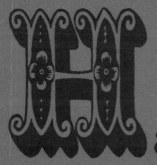

Happiness
is
a
bread
and butter
sandwich
folded over

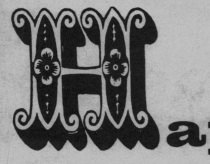

Happiness is knowing how to tie your own shoes

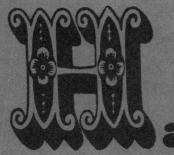

Happiness is walking in the grass in your bare feet.

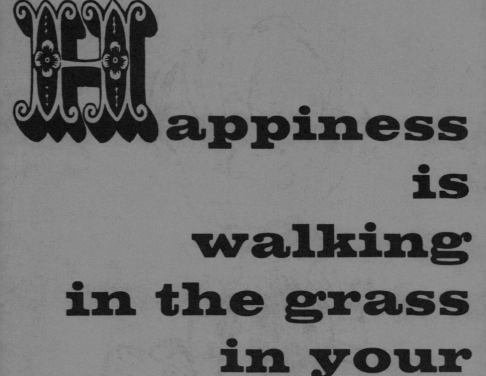

Happiness is eighteen different colors

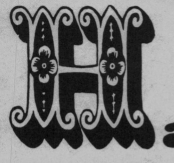

Happiness is a piece of fudge caught on the first bounce

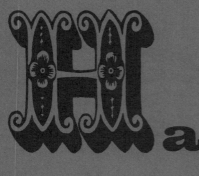

Happiness is finding the little piece with the pink edge and part of the sky and the top of the sailboat.

Happiness is finding out you're not so dumb after all

REPORT CARD
A

Happiness is
thirty-five cents
for the movie,
fifteen cents
for popcorn
and a nickel
for a candy bar.

Happiness is one thing to one person and another thing to another person.